MAGNIFICENT MAZES

Once you get in, you'll never get out!

Richard Burnie

RED
FOX

THE GREAT WALL OF CHINA
The imperial party travelling along the Great Wall
must avoid confrontation with the local farmers who
deal roughly with trespassers trampling on their crops.
Find a safe path for His Royal Highness to follow.

THE GREAT WALL OF CHINA

The Great Wall of China is the largest man-made structure in the world, built to defend the frontiers of China from the Yellow Sea to the mountains of Tibet. It took ten years to build – 214 to 204 BC – and is 1,500 miles long.

VENICE

Venice was built in 452 AD on low-lying islands in the Adriatic. Since its foundation it has been at the mercy of the tides and its own slowly sinking foundations. Despite heroic efforts the city is still regularly flooded.

THE SINKING OF THE TITANIC

In 1912 the *Titanic*, the world's then largest ocean liner and supposedly unsinkable, struck an iceberg in the North Atlantic and sank on its maiden voyage. 1,513 lives were lost. After this disaster there were sweeping changes made in standards of safety at sea.

CHRISTOPHER COLUMBUS

In 1492, believing that Asia could be reached by sailing westward, Columbus set off from Spain with three small ships to cross the Atlantic, making his first landfall in what is now the Bahamas – from where he discovered the mainland of America.

THE GREAT RETREAT FROM MOSCOW

Having made the disastrous decision to invade Russia in 1812, Napoleon was forced to retreat, defeated by both the Russian people and the Russian winter. 380,000 French soldiers died, only a handful making it back to France through the snow.

MOGUL TEMPLE

In India, the banks of the sacred river Ganges are crowded with ancient Hindu temples, some of which are two thousand years old.

MANHATTEN SKYSCRAPER

First built in the 1880s, it was not until the 1920s with advances in technology that skyscrapers became widespread. Manhattan boasts the most spectacular concentration in the world. Many riveters constructing the steel frameworks were Mohawk Indians. They were known as 'Girder Gorillas'.

THE LADY WITH THE LAMP

Appalled by the suffering of British soldiers wounded whilst fighting the Russians during the Crimean War, Florence Nightingale took a team of nurses to Scutari hospital in 1850 where she reduced the hospital death rate by 40%. She was the founder of nursing as a profession.

THE ROMAN ARENA

Arenas were the venues for a bloodthirsty mix of sport, combat and theatre. They were at their most popular between 200 BC and 400 AD and were found throughout the Roman empire.

THE EIFFEL TOWER

The unmistakable outline of the Eiffel Tower has dominated the skyline of Paris since 1889 when it was built to commemorate the World Fair. It is three hundred metres high.

PROHIBITION

In 1920 the sale and consumption of liquor was outlawed in the US. This led to bootlegging – the illegal distribution of liquor often illicitly distilled – and profiteering by criminal gangs. The act was repealed in 1933.

ANCIENT EGYPT

The sphinx was a mythological creature with a lion's body and a human head. In Egypt these colossal statues were built near the river Nile from around 2530 BC. Their exact purpose remains a mystery.

A Red Fox Book

Published by Random House Children's Books
20 Vauxhall Bridge Road, London SW1V 2SA

A division of The Random House Group Limited
London Melbourne Sydney Auckland
Johannesburg and agencies throughout the world

Copyright © Richard Burnie 1999

1 3 5 7 9 10 8 6 4 2

First published in Great Britain by
Jonathan Cape Limited, 1999
Red Fox edition 2000

Printed in Singapore by Tien Wah Press (PTE) Ltd

THE RANDOM HOUSE GROUP Limited Reg. No. 954009

www.randomhouse.co.uk

ISBN 0-09-926453-6

PROHIBITION

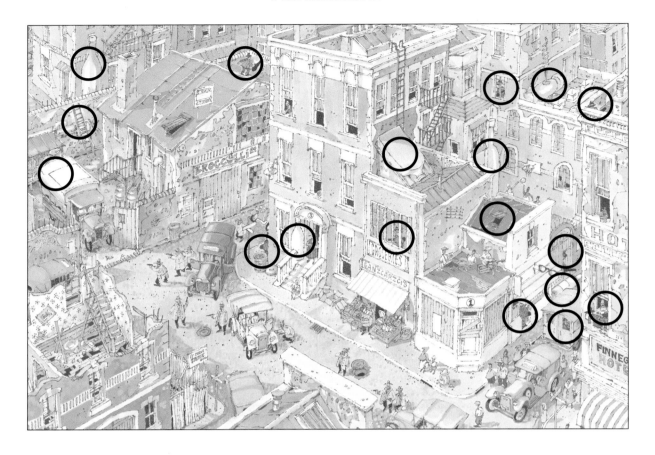

ANCIENT EGYPT

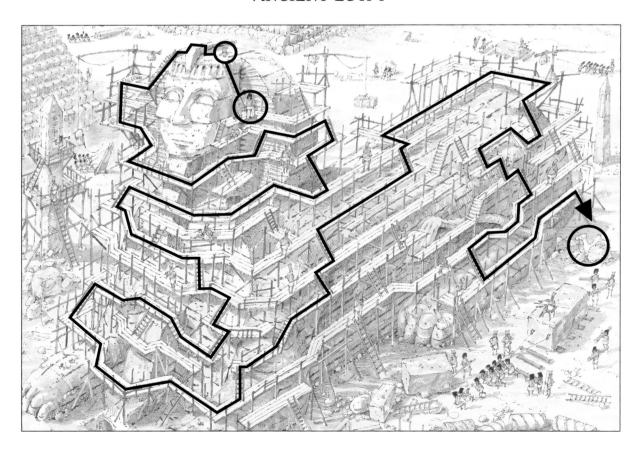

THE ROMAN ARENA

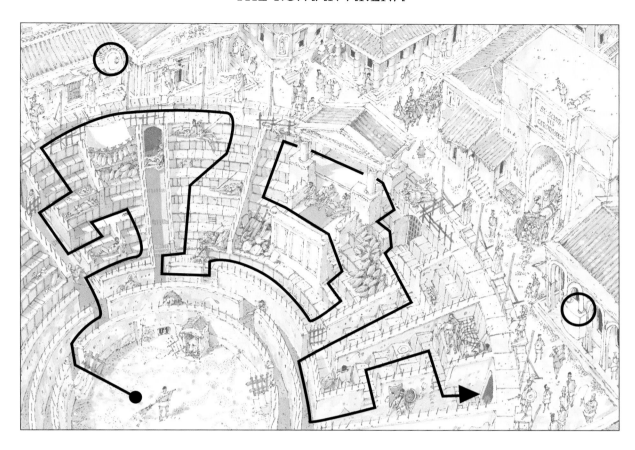

THE EIFFEL TOWER

MANHATTAN SKYSCRAPER

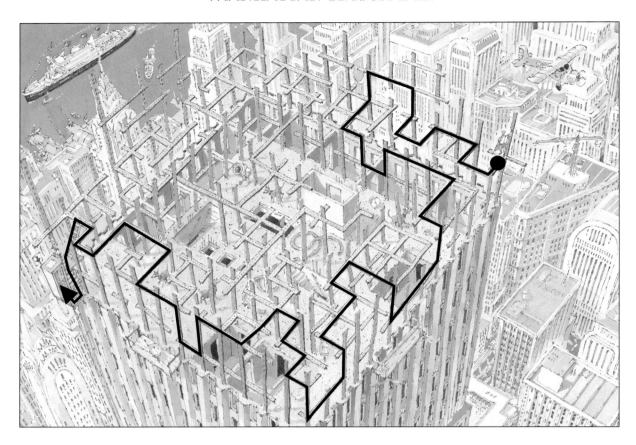

THE LADY WITH THE LAMP

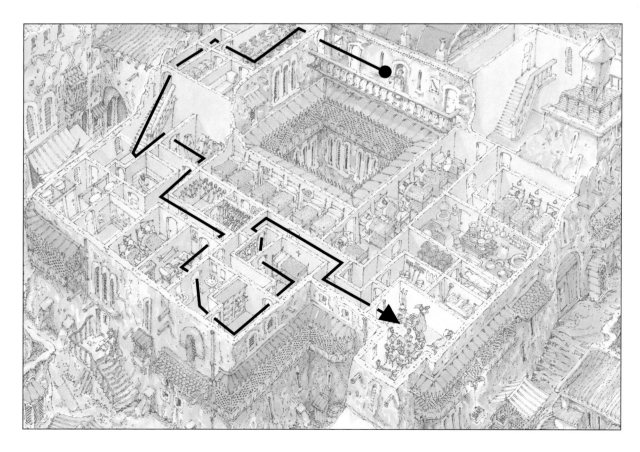

THE GREAT RETREAT FROM MOSCOW

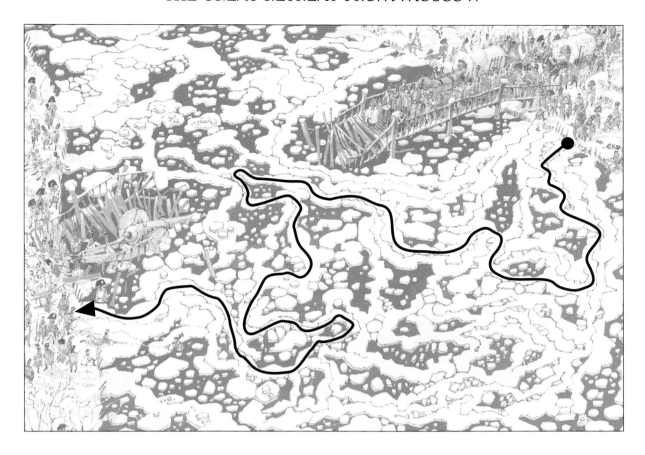

MOGUL TEMPLE

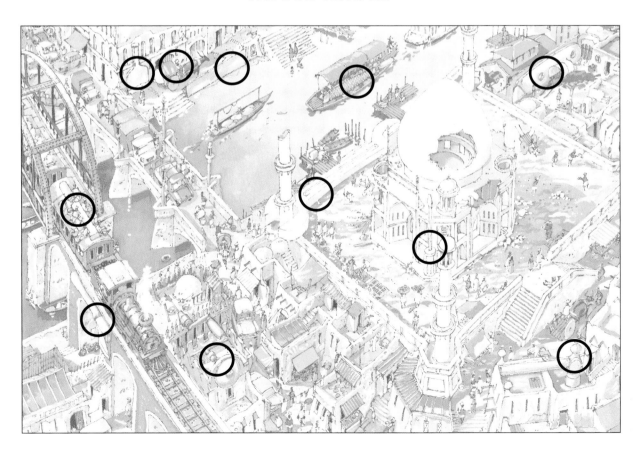

THE SINKING OF THE TITANIC

CHRISTOPHER COLUMBUS

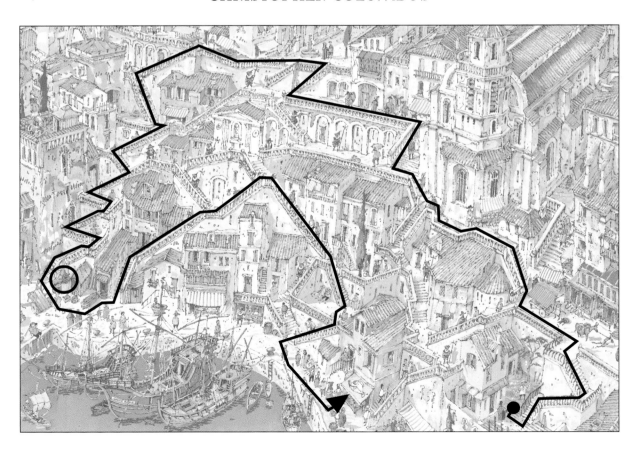

SOLUTIONS

THE GREAT WALL OF CHINA

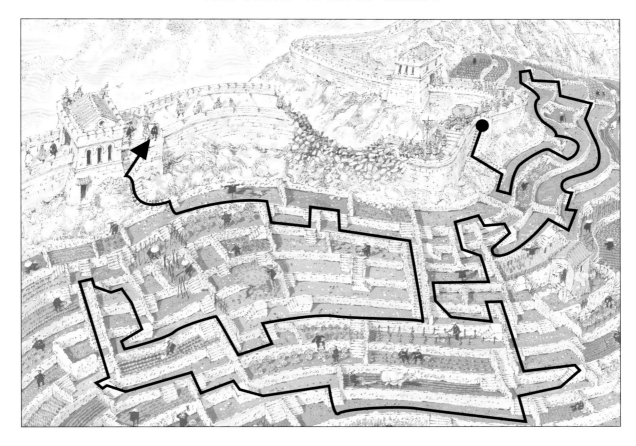

VENICE

ANCIENT EGYPT
On the Sphinx a slave makes a break for freedom with
the help of a disguise. As this disguise is flimsy, he must
not risk passing the slave drivers as he climbs down the
tomb. By which means of transport does he escape?

PROHIBITION
When the police raid the premises of the notorious
bootleggers, the Broccolli gang, there is no sign of
the ten gang members, nor of their half dozen
bottles of moonshine – nor of two vital pieces of
bootlegging equipment. Where are they?

THE EIFFEL TOWER
The Eiffel Tower is one of the biggest and most dangerous structures in the world to paint. Without climbing over the fresh red undercoat, how can the workman come to the rescue of his unfortunate colleague?

THE ROMAN ARENA
To escape the roving lions and reach one of the exits of the arena, the sweeper can climb up the seats but must not step over a sleeping gladiator. Keeping within the spiked barriers, which route should he take and where will he emerge? Find two objects hidden in the picture which would prevent the lions from getting out.

THE LADY WITH THE LAMP
Woken at dawn by the sounds of a party,
Florence Nightingale must silence the revellers.
Avoiding the wards of sleeping soldiers, what
route through the rooms would she take?

MANHATTAN SKYSCRAPER
After working late on the steel framework of the
building, a riveter finds himself alone on the site.
How can he get to the elevator – climbing up, down
and along the girders – without setting foot on the
level below which is patrolled by guard dogs?

MOGUL TEMPLE

Souvenir-hunters are dismantling the Mogul Temple. Find ten tools used by these vandals to carry out the demolition. Can you spot one of them making off with his prize?

THE GREAT RETREAT FROM MOSCOW
Napoleon's army retreating from Moscow discovers the
bridge across the river Berezina collapsed under the great
weight of a cannon. They must find a route to the far bank
without crossing the broken ice.

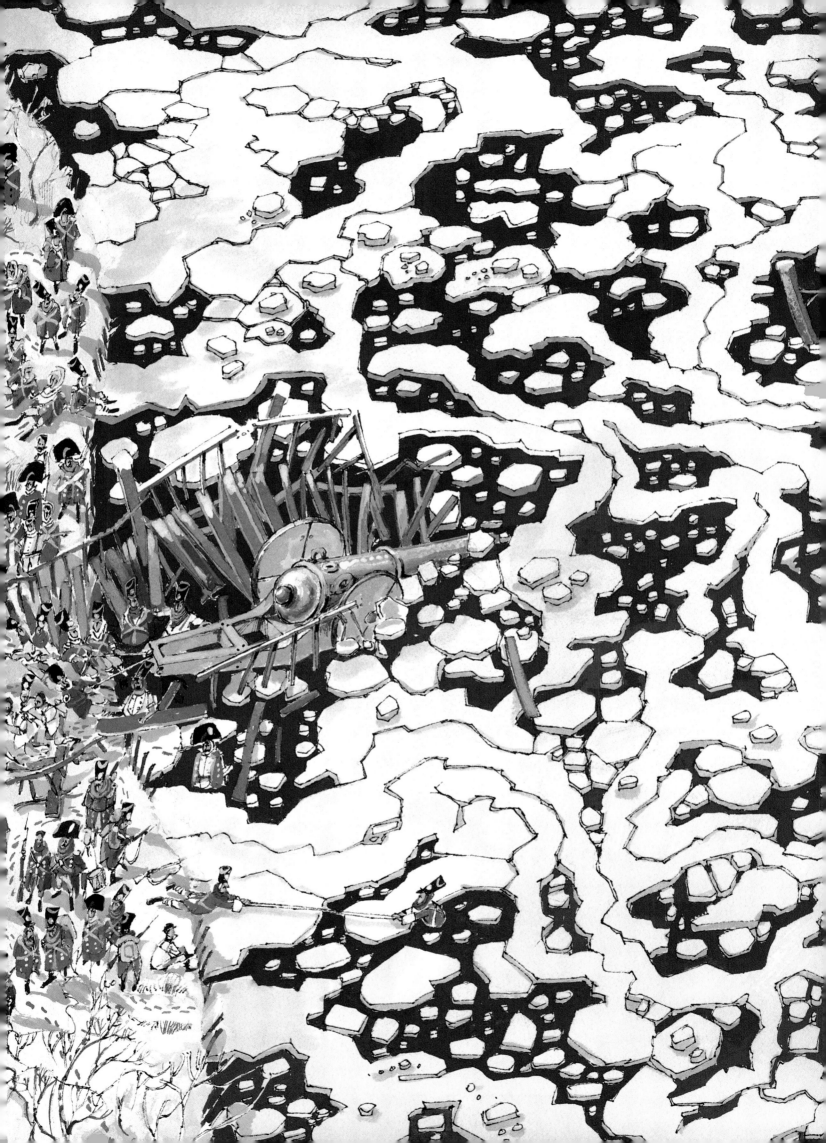

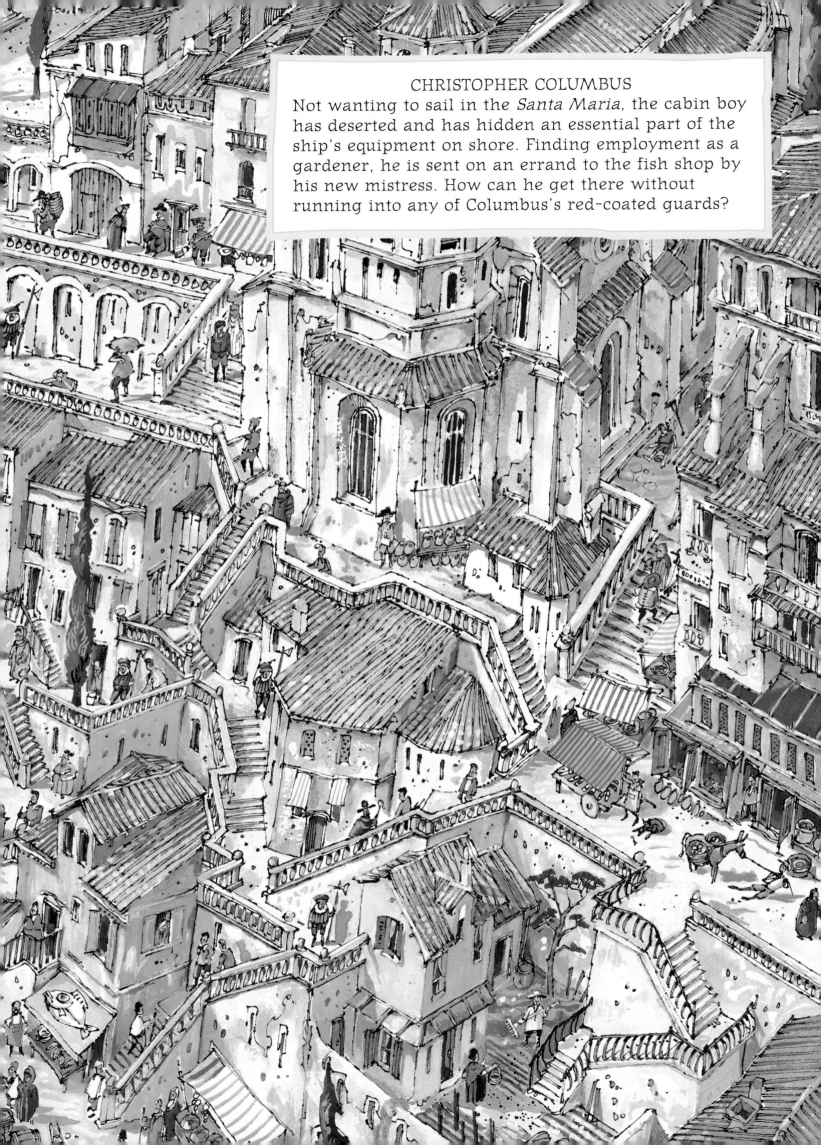

CHRISTOPHER COLUMBUS
Not wanting to sail in the *Santa Maria*, the cabin boy has deserted and has hidden an essential part of the ship's equipment on shore. Finding employment as a gardener, he is sent on an errand to the fish shop by his new mistress. How can he get there without running into any of Columbus's red-coated guards?

THE SINKING OF THE TITANIC

Survivors from the *Titanic* are picked up by the *SS North Star*. As the ship docks, *The Evening Echo* has three sensational headlines: 'Parents go to meet young triplets': 'Convict makes a daring escape': 'Two sets of identical twins reunited'. Are these statements true? Find something that could have prevented the *Titanic* sinking after it hit the iceberg!

NORTH STAR

VENICE

There are six cafés on the flooded piazza in Venice but very few customers. Just one waiter is on duty to serve them all. Carrying the drinks on his tray, he must not collide with anyone as he visits each café in a clockwise direction. Can you find his route over the temporary walkways – and can you spot the waiter's dog and a three-piece suite?